PERMACULTURE:
FINDING OUR OWN VINES AND FIG TREES

To Vanessa,
for gratitude
for your support —
Carol Coston, OP

SOR JUANA PRESS

Sor Juana Press is a project of Santuario Sisterfarm, a nonprofit organization rooted in the Texas Hill Country and grounded in the rich multi-cultural legacy of the Borderlands. Founded in 2002, Santuario Sisterfarm inspirits the work of transforming human relationships with Earth and other humans by moving from dominance to co-creative partnerships, drawing on insights from wisdom traditions, nature, the new science, and women's ways. Santuario Sisterfarm advances its mission by cultivating diversity–biodiversity and cultural diversity.

Sor Juana Press is dedicated to publishing the works of women–particularly women of color and women religious–on topics rooted in women's spirituality and relationship with Earth, *la Tierra, nuestra madre*.

The Press invokes the name and honors the memory of Sor Juana Inés de la Cruz (1648-1695), a Mexican nun, scholar, poet, playwright, musician, and scientist–a woman with a *sed de conocer* (a thirst for knowing)–who was silenced for advocating women's education. She is the first writer in the Americas to speak out in favor of a woman's right to learn and express concern about human depredation of the environment.

Other Books in the "Dominican Women on Earth" Series:

EARTH SPIRITUALITY: IN THE CATHOLIC AND DOMINICAN TRADITIONS
by Sharon Therese Zayac, O.P. (Issue No. 1, June 2003).

PERMACULTURE:
FINDING OUR OWN VINES AND FIG TREES

Carol Coston, O.P.

CONVERSATIO
Dominican Women on Earth

Issue No.2   August 2003

SOR JUANA PRESS
San Antonio, Texas

© 2003 Sor Juana Press

Edited by Elise D. García with Maureen Kelleher, R.H.S.M

Cover, including cover photograph, and book design by Susan E. Klein of Sister Creek Studios, San Antonio, Texas.
(www.sistercreekstudios.com)

Photography by the late Sarah Lawton Coston, Elise D. García, Susan E. Klein, and Mary Ragan

Printed by Crumrine Printers, Inc., San Antonio, Texas

This book is printed with soy inks on 100% post-consumer recycled paper, processed chorine-free, supplied by Dolphin Blue, a Dallas, Texas-based company specializing in environmentally responsible office products. (www.dolphinblue.com)

ISBN 0-9740243-1-7
ISSN 1543-978X

TABLE OF CONTENTS

About the Author viii

Sharing the Journey: Victory Garden to Sisterfarm..............1

Permaculture as an Earth Ethic 31

Thinking About the Whole 39

Permaculture in Practice I: A Tour of Sisterfarm 45

Permaculture in Practice II: Learning from Nature 63

Beyond Manicured Lawns 73

Finding Your Own Vine and Fig Tree...............................77

Notes..85

Recommended Resources 89

Postscript: About This Series 91

Ecology/Ecospirituality Centers 98

ABOUT THE AUTHOR

Carol Coston, O.P., an Adrian (Michigan) Dominican Sister, is the co-founder and co-director of Santuario Sisterfarm, a sanctuary for cultivating diversity in the Texas Hill Country. Prior to this, Carol founded and directed two Partners for the Common Good loan funds, raising more than $11 million in religious investments to provide low-interest credit to low-income communities in the United States, Latin America, and South Africa. The fund won the 2000 *Presidential Award for Excellence in Microenterprise*. In the early 1970s, Carol helped found, and for ten years served as the first director of, NETWORK: A National Catholic Social Justice Lobby, based in Washington, D.C. Carol was a founding member of the Adrian Dominican Sisters' Portfolio Advisory Board, serving as the Board's chair for twelve years and representing her congregation in dozens of shareholder resolutions on issues of justice in the global economy. Carol has served on numerous boards, including Red Tomato, which she currently chairs; ICCR (Interfaith Center on Corporate Responsibility), which she chaired for two years in the 1980s; Common Cause; Bread for the World; Mary's Pence; and Equal Exchange. She holds a Master of Art's degree in Speech and Drama and three honorary doctorates, and is the recipient of numerous honors and awards, including the Common Cause Citizenship Award and the Alexandrine Medal of St. Catherine's College. In January 2001, Carol became the first and only Catholic Sister ever to receive the *Presidential Citizens Medal*, given by the President of the United States "in recognition of U.S. citizens who have performed exemplary deeds of service for our nation."

SHARING THE JOURNEY:
VICTORY GARDEN TO SISTERFARM

And each sat under a vine and fig tree,
with no one to make them afraid.[1]

I have long loved this Scriptural passage, as it captures my view of a preferred world where all humans live in peace and lack nothing. Over the years, my understanding of the passage has expanded to embrace the inherent mutuality between the one who sits under the vine and fig tree and the flora that provides.

As I consider the journey that has led me to where I am today–living and working on a seven-acre piece of sacred Earth in the Hill Country of central Texas, where I tend my "vine and fig tree"–three gardening experiences stand out: a victory garden, a failed garden, and an organic garden.

VICTORY GARDEN

During World War II, my mother, Sally Coston, planted our first "Victory Garden" next to the garage of our house in West Palm Beach, Florida. Her garden mirrored thousands of other small plots started as a civilian response to the war effort, as suggested by President Roosevelt. The little gardens not only improved our eating, but also gave me an early experience of a group activity for the common good. It seemed as though everyone tried to cooperate doing whatever we could do to "help out" during the war. We children diligently collected scrap metal of all kinds for factories to recycle, and I remember squishing the packets of orange-yellow coloring into plastic bags of white lard to make it more palatable as ersatz margarine. In Florida we had to keep our blinds down when the lights were on and cover the car headlights halfway with black tape. This was to keep us out of sight of German submarines! My mother and her best friend were part of the Civil Air Patrol. Their job was to fly little Piper Cubs up and down the coast of Florida looking for the dreaded submarines. My mother swore she had spotted a sub, but no one would believe her.

FAILED GARDEN

Before I entered the Adrian Dominican Congregation at the age of nineteen, my whole life had been spent in West Palm Beach, Florida, where colorful flowers, bushes, and trees were in bloom year round. After my second bleak gray Michigan winter, I was feeling color-deprived, so I tried to start a garden near the novitiate. But being a "gardening novice," I made a major mistake. I had some vague notion that manure is good for growing, so I talked another novice into going with me to collect cow dung in neighboring fields. We managed to locate a fair amount and then proceeded to plant the seeds directly into it! Naturally, the hot manure burned up the little seeds.

Organic Garden

In 1973, I was living with ten other sisters near Catholic University in Washington, D.C. That spring, Adrian Dominican Anita Gerhardstein asked if anyone else was interested in having a garden. Since Anita knew a lot more about gardening than the city kid from Florida who burnt up seeds, I immediately and enthusiastically said yes. That "yes" continues to influence my life today because it launched a life-long interest in growing vegetables and herbs.

Soon someone introduced me to the magazine, *Organic Gardening and Farming*, and I became an avid student of organic methods: so fascinated by the concepts that my nights were spent reading THE ENCYCLOPEDIA OF COMPOSTING. My enthusiasm for organic methods, such as composting, must have been contagious because most of the summer interns who came to work with us at NETWORK, the national Catholic social justice lobby founded by nuns in 1971, have fond memories of our trips to the local stable to dig horse manure to add to the compost pile. (Maureen Kelleher, R.S.H.M., my good friend who was among the first members of the NETWORK staff and is now an immigration lawyer in Immokalee, Florida, described this as my "Tom Sawyer routine"–enticing people to come help because the project is presented as just the grandest thing to do of a Saturday, and it will be such fun.)

At that time I also learned a key principle of organic growing: "to give back to Earth as much or more than you take from her." This idea has grown in importance for me in the intervening years, as I observe our society's rapacious ways of treating Earth.

As I think back on these experiences and on the way I have changed over the past six and a half decades of my life, I recognize that my personal transformation has been more evolutionary than epiphanic. The movements have involved gradual changes, a sort of unfolding, rather than abrupt shifts –although, once I complete the internal shift, the external decisions to act on the internal change have always come quickly!

I trace the changes that have led me to where I am now to these gardening experiences and to four basic impulses that have been alive in me most of my life: a search for the Divine and meaningful ritual, a love of the outdoors, an aversion to racism and class prejudice coupled with an appreciation of diversity, and a commitment to social justice.

GOD QUEST AND RITUAL

As a child, I attended St. Ann's School in West Palm Beach, Florida, where the Adrian Dominican Sisters taught me. I loved the processions for Forty Hours (walking backwards and tossing flower petals), Benediction of the Blessed Sacrament, Solemn High Masses, and May Devotions, especially building my own May Altar and adorning it with flowers I picked myself. However, I really disliked the Friday Stations of the Cross during Lent and found creative ways to slip out of church and dart between cars and buses to get away from all that "At-the-cross-her-station-keeping…" mournfulness.

The many collections we took up at St. Ann's for the poor throughout the world certainly made us aware of the needs of others. Similarly, I have a strong memory of Sr. Immaculate, my eighth-grade teacher, who had the whole class stop what we were doing every time we heard an ambulance or fire engine. We would then pray for all those who were sick or in danger. Since St. Ann's was on the route to Good Samaritan Hospital, this practice was often repeated! Again, we were learning to think of others.

When I was a freshman at Florida State University (FSU), I was miserable, although by all outward appearances I was a model of success. I had many friends, dated a lot, made the dean's list, was both an FSU cheerleader and an acrobat in the FSU circus, and belonged to a highly regarded sorority. I now know that I was in a depression, and not for the last time. I attributed some of the misery to my lacking a clear goal in life or a strong passion for a particular area of study. The idea of getting married and raising a family wasn't enticing for me. I recall finding solace in early morning walks across the fairly deserted campus to attend Mass.

The summer between my freshman and sophomore years, my mother asked me to talk to a Jesuit friend of hers. I am sure she was perplexed by my sadness, during what was presumed to be the best time of my life–college days. In the course of my conversation with Father M.V. Jarreau, it became clear that I wanted to enter a religious community. When he asked why, I responded that I wanted to learn how to love God and that a convent seemed a good place in which to do it. Father Jarreau was a friend of Sr. Ann Catherine Gleason, O.P., the Adrian Dominican principal of Rosarian Academy, a boarding school in West Palm Beach sponsored by the congregation. Father Jarreau said, "Why don't I drive you up now to talk to her?" In about ten minutes, I was sitting across the desk from a nun I had never

met, beginning to plan a major change in my life–
entering the Adrian Dominican Congregation. I have
since told Rita Gleason that she never had a postu-
lant-to-be come around so quickly and with so little
effort on her part!

Being an Adrian Dominican for forty-eight years
has certainly nurtured my spirituality and my God
search, even though I am now living this out in
unexpected ways.

Particularly formative was my experience in

Behind Carol is the church in
Guayama, Puerto Rico, with its
bell tower.

Puerto Rico from 1957
to 1960, which had a
profound impact on
my spirituality and
sense of the sacred.
The church in
Guayama faced the
town square and was a
focal point for much of
the town's activities.
The church bell rang
every fifteen minutes,
reminding the people
of their religious her-
itage and calling them to a prayerful remembrance of
God's presence in their lives. (Although I heard tell
that one Adrian Dominican, a recent arrival at the
convent, who was being kept awake for hours by the

bell ringing, shouted out: "Who the hell cares that it's 3:00 a.m.!")

The Puerto Ricans seemed to connect with God as a beloved father–*papi*–and going to church was like visiting family in *papi's* house. It seemed to me that their relationship with God was less fearful, less formal, and more comforting, than the God I had grown up with–the One who knew everything you ever thought, who kept close track of all your actions, and whose displeasure could land you in big trouble. The Puerto Ricans had great devotion to Mary, to the Sacred Heart of Jesus, and to St. Anthony, the patron of the church. They also knew how to celebrate the various feast days, especially Holy Week.

Palm Sunday was like nothing I had ever seen!

Palm Sunday in Puerto Rico

The church was so packed with people carrying elaborately woven palm fronds that the priest couldn't even make it out of the sacristy to bless the palms. He just stood there looking perplexed and then, with a great circling of his arms back and forth, flung the holy water out into the crowd!

8

On Good Friday, hundreds of people participated in a lengthy procession that slowly poured down the church steps, wove around the town square, up and down nearby streets, and, much later, back into the church. Members of each parish organization walked together, often dressed alike, carrying a statue or representation of their sodality or club. We sisters were in our black cloaks, processing with our classroom students.

On Easter Sunday there was another procession, but this time the men followed a covered monstrance around one side of the plaza while the women went around the other side following the black-shrouded Mary. The band played somber music until the two processions met on the opposite side of the plaza. Then the black cloak was pulled off Mary and the purple cloth off the monstrance. The musicians began a celebratory piece for the Resurrection scene, and the men and women together processed back into church.

Throughout my life I have loved ritual. From the May Devotions of my childhood to present-day land blessings, rituals that celebrate the Divine with Earth's abundance—palm fronds, flowers, sage—and involve active participation through processions, sacred dance, drumming, or chanting are deep experiences of the Sacred for me.

As a child growing up in West Palm Beach, I was outside most of the time. Summers were spent in or around a pool or the ocean. I don't remember a time when I couldn't swim and I first jumped off a diving board at the age of three. In our neighborhood, which still had some wild places, such as a sandpit to explore, we always played outside games. I spent a lot time hanging out with the boys because they were more adventuresome. We all had ten-inch knives in holsters around our waists, as well as jackknives in our pockets. When walking to the sandpit you had to throw the big knife at a tree. If it landed correctly,

the knife would lodge and you could keep going. But if the knife didn't stick, you had to keep flipping it until it did.

We had a huge banyan tree in the front yard and we loved playing in it, especially imagining that we were Tarzan, Jane, and Boy, attempting to swing on the vines from the first-floor roof to the ground. On more than one occasion we knocked the breath out of ourselves when the vine didn't hold!

Five-year-old Carol

After I entered the convent, my outdoor activities were somewhat curtailed until I was missioned to Puerto Rico. My first year out of the novitiate was in Grosse Pointe, Michigan, and it was dreadful. Not only was I teaching second grade with no experience whatsoever, but the convent itself was a big, dark, looming building, filled with heavy furniture–all most gloomy to my Florida eyes. During the so-called recreation period at night, we played indoor games that I loathed, such as checkers or Monopoly, or put together some silly puzzle. I felt I was a teaching *and* a recreation failure!

One night I was so desperate for physical activity that a few of us younger nuns went up to the TV room where the usual scintillating options were to watch Bishop Sheen or Lawrence Welk. (No wonder I have never really warmed up to TV.) But this night I offered to teach everyone how to stand on her head, no easy feat with the full habit! We pinned our habits together to keep them from falling down when our legs were up. Soon we were in gales of laughter that brought the superior upstairs. She must have suspected something was amiss because neither Sheen nor Welk were ever very funny.

Aversion to Racism and Class Prejudice, and Appreciation of Diversity

My parents would never allow us to talk about other races, especially African Americans, in derogatory ways. I remember being perplexed by the

"White Only" and "Colored Only" signs on public drinking fountains and at the train station. On buses I would deliberately sit in the back. This was probably not a precocious demonstration of anti-racism, but rather the action of a headstrong little girl who didn't like to be told where she could sit. But as I later learned, I would never suffer the consequences of not complying, as would a Black person.

When we were preparing for First Communion, several Black students from the catechism classes taught by Adrian Dominicans came to school with us for about a week or so. I remember being thrilled with their energy, high spirits, and athletic ability. At last I had some girls who weren't afraid to tear around the schoolyard playing no-holds-barred tag. Plus, now I was playing with girls who could run as fast, or faster, than I. When we finally made our First Communion and they were no longer in class with us, I felt a real loss of their companionship.

My first strong memory of class prejudice was on Easter Sunday when I was in the eighth grade. My friend Mary, who lived in the projects in a poor part of town, came to Mass in her old and faded school uniform and beat-up shoes. We were standing next to each other in the choir loft and I could hear the snickers and see the finger pointing of girls all around us in their new Easter dresses. I felt so angry at their sense of superiority just because they had on new dresses, and I felt so sad about Mary's hurt feelings. It seemed unfair that a person's clothes could cause such a negative and mean response. That incident affirmed my distaste for dressing up.

A decade later, as a junior professed sister missioned to teach in Guayama, Puerto Rico, I was aware of the great variety of skin color among the students I taught. I noticed that, by and large, it didn't seem to make a big difference in their acceptance of each other. Those whose ancestry was more immediately traceable to Spain, however, somehow let you know that. But the prejudice I *did* notice came from a few of our Dominican sisters from the United States. They would make teasing, but probably hurtful, remarks around the young sisters in our community who were from Puerto Rico or the Dominican Republic, poking fun at their accents, mistakes in grammar, funny word choices, or cultural differences. Since I was the only North American sister who hadn't made final vows, I sat at the end of the table with all my young Latina sisters (the hierarchy of seating being by "age in religion"). We also spent a lot of time together at chores and recreation, and I resented what was happening to them. Here they were speaking a second language to accommodate the rest of us North Americans, most of whom, including myself, only spoke English or a halting Spanish.

In fairness, I need to add that we North Americans also told stories about the blunders we made in Spanish. Some of the biggest bloopers had become a part of the new folklore of our sisters in the islands.

On a larger societal level, it was in Puerto Rico–and in the Dominican Republic where we spent the summers–that I first became aware of the creeping cultural invasion of U.S. music, films, and products of all kinds. Intuitively, I felt that this was a loss for the peoples of Puerto Rico and the Dominican Republic: to see so much of the richness of their heritage being engulfed by this giant from the north.

My apprehension about the impact of this cultural invasion was probably rooted in my profound love of Puerto Rico and the Dominican Republic. It was the first time I ever lived outside the United States, and I grew to have a deep appreciation of all that was different about these people and their bioregions.

I admired the strong family ties, the gracious hospitality, the laughter and music. I was intrigued by the great variety of fruit, by the egg and vegetable vendors calling out their wares early in the morning, and by the *pasta de guava con queso*, a gelatinous form of guava fruit served with a local white cheese. Doña Fela was our cook and I loved being in the kitchen with her, watching her skillfully prepare a diversity of dishes, all delicious.

The Dominican convent in Guayama was on the third floor of the school. The large and light-filled living room had tile floor–great for dancing, which many of the sisters, but especially Margarita Ruíz, O.P. and I, loved to do. Margot taught me the merengue, mambo, cha-cha, salsa, and together we developed a bi-cultural version of the jitterbug.

My wonderful years in Puerto Rico and the Dominican Republic came to an abrupt end on May 17, 1960. The phone rang at midnight and I happened to answer it. Doris Downey, a good friend of my family, delivered the news that Cocky (what everyone called my father, Clarence) had been killed in a plane accident in the Bahamas. All she knew was that the four-passenger plane he piloted took off from a makeshift runway lit by car headlights, and went up about 500 feet before crashing down into the water. He and his three passengers were all dead. Doris said my mother was in shock.

I was stunned and felt numb as all the sisters woke up and began feverish preparations to have me driven across the island to the convent in Santurce and onto the next plane for Florida. As we headed out around 2:00 a.m., I had a terrible feeling that it was all a nightmare, that this accident hadn't really happened, and that I had gotten everyone up for nothing. But it wasn't a bad dream. The terrible accident happened, and I never went back to Puerto Rico. The sisters packed up my classroom and sent my clothes to Florida, where the congregation missioned me so that I could be closer to my mother, as we all recovered from the shock and loss.

Four years later, in 1964, I was sent to the western part of the state to join the faculty of Tampa Catholic High School, a new school that the Adrian Dominican Sisters were asked to staff. It was a time of the civil rights struggle and the war in Vietnam. Tampa Catholic was integrated, but there were not great numbers of Black students enrolled. I made it my personal mission to try to encourage all the Black students to become involved in the National Forensics League (NFL) program that I founded at the school. I thought that they, along with the other students in the program, would be better prepared to assume leadership roles as adults if they felt comfortable as public speakers.

After six years at Tampa Catholic, where I had also created programs for our students to tutor Black kids in inner-city elementary schools and had developed cross-cultural curricula for all my classes, I felt a call to work directly in the Black community. I asked my provincial if I could do this and she encouraged me to try to find a job that would enable this to happen.

In 1970, I was hired by the Neighborhood Youth Corps, one of the federally funded agencies established as part of President Johnson's "War on Poverty," and initially lived in St. Rose's Convent in Miami Shores where my Adrian Dominican friend

Jean Rosaria served as superior and principal of St. Rose's Elementary School. In 1971, another Adrian Dominican Sister, Kathleen Gannon, and I moved from St. Rose's into a housing project sponsored by the Kiwanis Club and the Methodist Church in a largely Black neighborhood in Fort Lauderdale. It was the first time I lived outside a convent since entering religious life sixteen years earlier.

As an administrator of the Neighborhood Youth Corps high-school dropout program in Ft. Lauderdale, I was able to facilitate young people getting summer jobs, high-school equivalency courses, help with day care for their children, and some job training. But what I learned from this experience was how triply hard it was to be a Black single parent in this society. When you are poor, uneducated (in a formal way), and a young mother, everything conspires against you.

Around this time, I finished my master's thesis, which was titled *Black Theatre in the 1960s*. The paper compared the contents, language, values, and perspective of Black plays and playwrights with the findings of the Kerner Report, which was issued in 1968 by a federal commission that investigated the urban riots that had taken place in major U.S. cities during the previous three summers. These experiences helped me better understand the damaging and hurtful aspects of racism and prejudice, and heightened my appreciation for the cultural and religious contributions of African Americans.

The experiences also awakened in me a keen awareness of the need for systemic change. It was clear we lived in a society that was denying people the right to sit under their own vine or fig tree and to live without fear.

COMMITMENT TO JUSTICE

While we were living in the housing projects, Kathy Gannon and I got involved in a coalition effort to pass an open-housing ordinance to stop discrimination against Black people who were trying to buy houses in white neighborhoods. We also participated in efforts to pressure the city into opening up additional polling booths in Black neighborhoods to make it more convenient and less intimidating to vote.

In December 1971, Kathy was invited to a meeting of Catholic sisters in Washington, D.C., to see if there was a role for women religious to play in the political process. With my provincial's support, I tagged along, uninvited. As a result of my attending that meeting, I ended up becoming one of the forty-seven founders of a national Catholic social justice lobby we called "NETWORK." Soon thereafter, I was asked to be its first director.

Within three months, I moved from Florida to Washington and spent the next ten years writing and lobbying on national legislation, giving workshops on political action at the congressional and state levels, developing charts and articles on the social encyclicals as they applied to public policy, and representing NETWORK on many coalition efforts aimed at bringing about systemic change.[2]

In 1974, during the annual NETWORK summer seminar, I was part of a group of two dozen Adrian Dominicans who strategized on how to encourage our congregation to use justice as a criterion in examining our investment portfolio. Soon after, a resolution establishing the "Portfolio Advisory Board" was adopted by the Chapter of Affairs, or legislative body, of the Adrian Dominican Sisters, and the congregation began the "social screening" of our investments. I served on the board from 1975 until 1991, as chair for thirteen of those years and as executive director for several others.[3]

Some fifteen years after that summer strategizing session, the experiences I gained in the intervening years in screening investments, corporate responsibility, and alternative investing led me to establish, in response to a request from the Christian Brothers Investment Services (CBIS), an alternative loan fund under their auspices. My work in social justice moved out of the legislative and into the financial arena.

During the next eleven years I worked with over 100 religious congregations or institutes that chose to invest in the two "Partners for the Common Good" loan funds we created. With more than $11 million in investments, the Partners' board and I were able to make dozens of loans to low-income housing groups, minority-owned credit unions, and small and cooperatively owned businesses in the United States and Central America, as well as to micro-enterprises in Bolivia, Ecuador, Haiti, and South Africa.

The loans were helpful to the borrowers and all the investors were paid back their capital investment in full, plus yearly interest payments. However, after all those years of reading loan applications, pouring over financials, processing loans, monitoring loan repayments, reading accountability reports, and logging over 100,000 air miles annually in site visits, I was tired and yearned to be grounded in one place.

Also, and significantly, my sense of "justice" had gradually been expanding beyond the social and financial arenas to encompass a concern about justice for all life on Earth. This yearning, no doubt, was planted in me early on back in our family's victory garden and grew particularly while doing organic gardening during my NETWORK years.

We on the NETWORK staff often worked at articulating our individual and collective visions of a more just society. The influence of my organic gardening practices is evident in the personal vision I articulated in this 1977 reflection:

> My vision of the world is seen through the lens of food production and distribution. … [In Genesis, God said,] "See, I give you all the seed-bearing plants that are upon the Earth and all the trees with seed-bearing fruit; this shall be your good."

> In Micah we find a vision of a world without war, where "each person shall sit under their own vine and fig tree, with no one to trouble them. The mouth of Yahweh Sabaoth has spoken it."

> Currently, much food production is viewed as big business for profit—not as a response to each person's right to eat. Efficiency is measured by total profits rather than by the quality of the food or the condition of the soil. The land is often abused rather than "cared for." Seed-bearing plants are not seen as a gift from God to be shared but as the first step in a vertical integration of agribusiness.

Ever since I became hooked on organic gardening, I had dreamed of living someplace where I could literally put down roots, and put all that I knew about sustainable agriculture into practice. My dream place would be between ten to fifteen acres in size, with a creek, a long growing season, and fairly easy access to an airport (as I was usually holding jobs and had congregational commitments that required much travel). I envisioned an orchard, large vegetable gardens, an herb garden, a greenhouse, several compost bins, and worm bins.

The vine and fig tree passage that had long caught my imagination is one of multiple references to those plants in the Hebrew Scriptures, some as warnings and others as promises. I saw the image in several layers: at the legislative level, I wanted policies for land reform and sustainable agriculture; at the societal level, I wanted all people to have their own metaphorical vine and fig tree and to live in safety; and at a personal level, I wanted a real fig tree and a real grape vine! I also wanted to find a community that could celebrate in ritual our fruitful Earth and the Spirit flowing through all life forms.

In 1985, after I left NETWORK, Adrian Dominican Sisters Maureen Fenlon, Corinne Florek, and I worked together on founding "Lydia," a nonprofit named in honor of the enterprising woman mentioned in *The Acts of the Apostles 16:* "One of these women was called Lydia...who was in the purple dye trade."

We were committed to working with women in worker-owned cooperatives. At a planning meeting, the three of us reflected on our personal dream of what we hoped a "Lydia Center" would look like in three-to-five years. This is what I envisioned:

> The buildings are finished in a natural sur-rounding–trees, herb gardens, vegetable plots, hopefully water. Atmosphere exudes warmth and welcome–gives strong pres-ence of women who are confident, compe-tent, proud of their history, aware of global links, concerned about injustice, chal-lenged to keep learning and growing. Décor is simple and tasteful, space for large-group meetings and small classes/discussions. Room to sleep for 20 to 30–emphasis on small numbers. Library and music reflective of values and diversity. Professional materi-als well-organized, useful and accessible. Relaxed environment. Lots of living things –animals and plants and fruit trees.

It is a source of constant amazement and bub-bling-up gratitude that in 1992, when Elise García, Nancy Sylvester, I.H.M., and I moved to Texas, we found just such a place, one hour's drive northwest of San Antonio. Although it is only seven acres in size and can accommodate around a dozen people (who don't mind sharing space!), it does have a creek! The animals came later as did all the gardens, but the essence of the dream was here in a place we call "Sisterfarm." Nancy lived with us during her sabbatical, following a ten-year stint as the second director of NETWORK, and then moved to Michigan in 1994 when she was elected vice president of her Monroe-based congregation near Detroit.

We had the first of many "Sisterfarm Workdays" on two Saturdays in November 1992. Inviting our new San Antonio friends and acquaintances from the law school where Elise worked and the Center for Women where I had my office, we put the Tom Sawyer routine into practice and a wonderful group of supporters emerged. The first workdays involved clearing mounds of tangled cedar and other brush and relieving a beautiful ravine that had been used as a dumpsite of some 150 bags of garbage. In addition to the three of us and the nucleus of our San Antonio support community, two university professors from afar joined in the ravine clean up: Dr. Cheryl Rodríguez, my former student at Tampa Catholic, now a cultural anthropologist in the Africana Studies Program at the University of South Florida in Tampa, and Dr. Marit Bakke, a sociologist at the University of Bergen in Norway. Later projects involved such activities as fencing in an orchard, building decks and a tower, and creating raised vegetable beds.

In the clearing and building, and the shared meals, dancing, and laughter that would be a part of each of these workdays, a strong sense of community and wonderful friendships were formed during the course of that decade. We also shared rituals, such as the memorable blessing of the land at Sisterfarm celebrated with our San Antonio friends together with the twelve members of my Adrian Dominican "Hildegard" Mission Group.[4]

In 2000, as the second Partners for the Common Good fund was winding to a close, Elise and I began planning the creation of an Earth-focused nonprofit organization, something we each had in mind when we moved to Texas. Invoking the Spanish word for "sanctuary," we called the organization-to-be "Santuario Sisterfarm," and in 2001, joined by our friend, María Antonietta Berriozábal, a longtime San Antonio community activist and the first Mexican-American woman in the United States to serve on the city council of a major U.S. city–we three incorporated the new nonprofit.

The legal papers were drafted pro bono by a group of students at the University of Oregon School of Law, under the direction of their professor, Barbara Bader Aldave. It was Barbara, former president of the board of NETWORK, who enticed Elise to come to San Antonio in the first place.

In January 2002, the founding board of Santuario Sisterfarm had its first meeting. Along with me, the founders included:

- Janie Barrera–president of ACCION Texas, an award-winning alternative loan fund serving low-income communities throughout Texas;

- María Antonietta Berriozábal–San Antonio community leader and former U.S. representative of the Inter-American Commission on Women of the Organization of American States, former U.S. delegate to the United Nation's Fourth World Conference on Women in Beijing, and former San Antonio city council-woman;

- Elizabeth Blissman, Ph.D.–director of the Center for Service and Learning at Oberlin College and lecturer in the Environmental Studies Department, also a co-member of the Loretto Community;

- Elise D. García–consultant to nonprofit organizations, former vice president of Common Cause, and former director of communications and development at St. Mary's University School of Law;

• Barbara Matteson, O.P.–director of finance for the Houston Dominicans, former prioress of the Dominican Sisters of Edmonds (Washington), and founding president of the National Association of Treasurers of Religious Institutions (NATRI); and

• Patricia Siemen, O.P., J.D.–director of the Environmental Ethics Institute at Miami-Dade Community College and former vicaress of the Adrian Dominican Sisters.

At that meeting, we articulated the following mission for Santuario Sisterfarm, a ministry that I have described as my fourth, and probably last.

Rooted in the Texas Hill Country and grounded in the rich multicultural legacy of the Borderlands, Santuario Sisterfarm inspirits the work of transforming human relationships with Earth and among ourselves by moving from domination to co-creative partnerships, drawing on insights from wisdom traditions, nature, the new science, and women's ways.

27

We advance Santuario Sisterfarm's mission by *cultivating diversity*–biodiversity and cultural diversity. The projects we have undertaken to cultivate diversity include the *Rosa y Martín Seed Project, Latinas in the Borderlands,* and *Sor Juana Press*.

The *Seed Project*–named in honor of Rosa de Lima and Martín de Porres, Dominicans who stood with indigenous people against colonial powers in sixteenth-century Peru–is about standing with economically impoverished people against the predatory practices of multinational corporations that are usurping seed lines developed over centuries by small farmers around the world. It involves educational efforts to address the dangerous loss of biodiversity and exploitation of poor people worldwide when they are made dependent on yearly purchases of hybrid seeds sold by multinationals. This year we encouraged other ecology centers and individuals to plant heirloom tomatoes and non-genetically modified soybeans. Here at Sisterfarm, we focus on planting a diversity of organically grown heirloom seeds.

Through the *Latinas in the Borderlands* project, Santuario Sisterfarm is embarking on a journey–an eco-ethno-spiritual quest–with Latinas to create a multilingual, multiracial, multicultural space where *mujeres* can go deep into the spirit of ancestral connections to the land, cultural traditions, women's ways of knowing, and struggles for justice.

28

And through *Sor Juana Press*, we are promoting the ecological and spiritual writings of women of color and women religious. A small publishing house named after Sor Juan Inés de la Cruz, a Mexican nun, scholar, and poet of the seventeenth century, *Sor Juana Press* is publishing two series of "little books." One set, written by Dominican women (including me, with this book!) is titled *Dominican Women on Earth*; the other, written by Latinas, is titled *La Mujer y La Tierra.*

Finally, at the core of its mission, Santuario Sisterfarm also strives to serve as a model for light living on Earth by incorporating permacultural and other sustainable designs and practices on site–planting vines and fig trees, among other things.

Sisterfarm in 1992

Permaculture is an Earth ethic that embraces the inherent mutuality between the one who sits and the plants that provide in the Scriptural passage about the vine and fig tree. The term was coined in the early 1970s by Australian Bill Mollison, who writes:

> Permaculture (**perma**nent agri**culture**) is the conscious design and maintenance of agriculturally productive ecosystems, which have the diversity, stability, and resilience of natural ecosystems. It is the harmonious integration of landscape and people providing their food, energy, shelter, and other material and non-material needs in a sustainable way. Without permanent agriculture there is no possibility of a stable social order.[5]

Permaculture is modeled on Earth's ecosystems, natural communities of wild plants and animals such as forests, marshes, and meadows. The basic idea is to create stable, diverse, resilient, and edible ecosystems, often referred to as edible landscapes.

Permaculture's preferred world vision would be to put food production back into the hands of local farmers and peasants, with the support they need to sustain it.[6] Cities and communities would be arranged in such a way that people would have direct access to locally grown food instead of importing it from thousands of miles away. Tax breaks, water subsidies, price and other supports would be designed to aid small farmers rather than agribusiness. And government would encourage an ethic of buying locally to help keep small farmers in business and able to earn a living.

I have never met Bill Mollison, but I know from reading his books and watching his videos that we have a lot in common. First, we are around the same age. Next, we were both social activists in the late 1960s and early 1970s, and felt similar frustrations. He rejected "military adventurism, the bomb, ruthless land exploitation, the arrogance of polluters, and a general insensitivity to human and environmental needs."[7] These issues were a big part of NETWORK's legislative agenda.

From 1972 to 1974, Mollison and his colleague, David Holmgren, developed the concepts of permaculture as an interdisciplinary Earth science, and then spent the next four years applying the principles of permaculture in a species-rich garden. The first book, PERMACULTURE ONE, was published in 1978, and the next, PERMACULTURE TWO, in 1979.

Mollison resigned from his teaching position in 1979 and, as he writes in a third book, INTRODUCTION TO PERMACULTURE, published in 1991:

> ...[I] threw myself at an advanced age into an uncertain future. I decided to do nothing else but to try to persuade people to build good biological systems. I designed quite a few properties, and existed for a while by catching fish and pulling potatoes.[8]

In 1980, I had a four-month sabbatical from NETWORK and spent six weeks of it pursuing my love affair with organic gardening at Rodale Research Farm. I was a hired hand, assigned to the greenhouse and demonstration herb garden. Although I was paid little, I learned a lot, and not just about organic methods. Having been immersed in Washington politics for years, I was naturally interested in the Democratic primary in Pennsylvania when Ted Kennedy was running. The morning after the primary I was in the tool shed waiting to go to work and listening to the other farm hands talk. The topic that morning was not the presidential election results, but figuring out what was wrong with the calibration on the manure spreader! (Some might say it was the same subject.)

Two years later, in 1982, after ten intense years as director of NETWORK, I asked my congregation if I could study agriculture. The study program was approved, but after a few courses at the University of Maryland focused on agribusiness methodology, I sought alternative approaches. I ended up interning at two intentional communities–Koinonia Farm in Georgia and Springtree Community in Virginia –both devoted to organic methods and to creating new forms of communal life.

My living and gardening with younger people during this time was somewhat akin to "throwing myself at an advanced age into an unknown future." I, too, had grown frustrated and disheartened working within the political system and wanted to garden fulltime, immersing myself in various approaches to sustainable food growing. Being actively involved in creating new ways of living on Earth was definitely more inviting than devoting my energies to fighting bad public policy during those Reagan years.

For nearly two decades, Mollison traveled throughout the world sharing permaculture methods and learning from local gardeners and farmers about what worked best in their particular bioregions.[9] From these travels and visits with former students, Mollison and his colleagues developed ways to implement an ethic of Earth care, which resonates deeply with me.

Among the Earth-care values they began to promote are the following:

- Think about the long-term consequences of your actions. Plan for sustainability.

- Where possible use species native to the area, or those naturalized species known to be beneficial. ...

- Cultivate the smallest possible land area. Plan for small-scale, energy-efficient *intensive* systems rather than large-scale, energy-consuming *extensive* systems.

- Be diverse, polyculture (as opposed to monoculture). This provides stability and helps us to be ready for change, whether environmental or social.

- Increase the sum of yields: look at the *total* yield of the system provided by annuals, perennials, crops, trees, and animals. Also, regard energy saved as a yield.

- Use low-energy environmental (solar, wind, and water) and biological (plant and animal) systems to conserve and generate energy.

• Bring food-growing back into the cities and towns, where it has always traditionally been in sustainable societies. ...

• Reforest the Earth and restore fertility to the soil.

• Use everything at its optimum level and recycle all wastes.

• See solutions, not problems [*e.g.*, "You don't have a snail problem, you have a shortage of ducks!"].

• Work where it counts (plant a tree where it will survive; assist people who want to learn).[10]

In all of these practices, cooperation–not competition–is the key.[11]

Permaculture's Earth-care ethic has special resonance with me because it embodies much of what I hold as spiritual truth–particularly its inherent call for us to live in consideration of the common good of *all* creation. It also resonates with me because it offers practical ways–described in the ensuing chapters of this book–to respond to the imperatives of the "new story of the universe."

In August 2001, I participated in "Exploring a New Cosmology," a program at Genesis Farm–an Earth-literacy center founded in 1980 by Caldwell Dominican Miriam Therese MacGillis that has inspired so many us. The program involves intensive study of the "new story of the universe," which is the rich narrative that science is now able to provide, *for the first time in human history*, about the origins of the universe.

The new story traces the beginnings of the universe back to an unfathomably dense "singularity" that some fourteen billion years ago exploded in what is popularly called the "big bang." It was an extraordinary flaring forth of primordial material that created time and space as it expanded in all directions and, over deep time, evolved, with astonishing creativity, into stars and galaxies, oceans and mountains, frogs and people.

We participated in a "Cosmic Walk" several times, at each pass gaining a slightly better sense of the deep time involved in the universe's evolution and of the miniscule eye-blink at the tail end of this epic story that is the sum total of human history. We engaged in daily readings–including the works of Thomas Berry, Joanna Macy, and Brian Swimme –about the story of our universe and the extraordinary challenges that we humans are now posing to life on Earth, where no plant or creature on the planet is safe from the adverse effects of our presence.

I must admit that I experienced some terror in trying to fathom a universe that contains billions of galaxies and each galaxy, billions of stars. And I was made heartsick by reading books and articles and watching videos about the devastating impact that we humans are now having on our home planet, Earth. I found comfort in the early morning body prayers, the elegantly prepared vegetarian meals, sharing reflections with the other women, and meandering around the farm's 150-plus acres, observing the abundance and diversity of nature. And I left with a commitment to bring the learnings of Genesis Farm to Santuario Sisterfarm, the new nonprofit organization that we were forming in Texas.

Applying permacultural practices at Santuario Sisterfarm is a key way of fulfilling that commitment. While the idea of living in a universe that has billions of galaxies still fills me with terror, I find great comfort in thinking that a handful of the soil we have enriched with compost year after year at Sisterfarm contains billions of microorganisms quietly at work. The new story of the universe teaches me that my fate, ultimately, is linked to the fate of those microorganisms. Permaculture teaches me a way to live, respond, and act to support the life of those microorganisms and, by extension, the life of the vine and the fig tree—and of those who rest under them.

THINKING ABOUT THE WHOLE

The concepts embodied in permaculture are not new. Native peoples have long held the wisdom that we westerners must grow into, if life on Earth is to survive. It is a wisdom that is also at the heart of most the world's religious traditions–recognizing our interconnectedness and the Oneness of all. The scientific story of the universe, which tells that all life emerged from a singularity, Oneness, affirms this ancient insight.

Now we are being called to live it.

In a speech to the United Nations, Oren Lyons, Faithkeeper of the Onondaga Nation, spoke to this:

I do not see a delegation for the four-footed. I see no seat for the eagles. We forget and we consider ourselves superior, but we are after all a mere part of the Creation. And we must continue to understand where we are. And we stand between the mountain and the ant, somewhere and there only, as part and parcel of the Creation. It is our responsibility, since we have been given the minds to take care of these things.[12]

I began a self-study of permaculture as a design system two years ago, about the same time that María Antonietta Berriozábal, Elise García and I filed to incorporate Santuario Sisterfarm.

One of the organization's goals is to make this place an example of applied permaculture, of living lightly on the land, of Earth care. It is a natural unfolding of the practices we had applied over the previous ten years at Sisterfarm, including a commitment to use organic methods and to reuse and recycle as much as possible. It is an intentional way of living that embraces the imperative of the emerging universe story that we humans find a new way of living and being part of the whole Earth community, moving away from domination-over to partnership-with all life forms.

One of permaculture's design concepts is to think about the whole–your home and land–and to plan the layout by dividing the whole into a series of zones or concentric circles, emanating from the center, the house. What is situated and where depends on how many times you need to visit the site. This is in keeping with the permacultural idea that energy saved, including your own energy, is a "yield."

People who live in urban or suburban areas usually have only one or two zones to consider. In rural areas, a farm can have up to five zones, as follows:

Zone Zero is the central circle–the place where you spend your most time–the house.

Zone One is the circle immediately surrounding Zone Zero–the area closest to the house in the surrounding yard. This is an area of intense use and a center of activity. Culinary herbs, salad greens, other vegetables, seedlings, and young trees go here.

Zone Two is the circle beyond Zone One–the area beyond the surrounding yard, for those who have larger properties (or, for suburban dwellers, the areas in the yard furthest from the house). This area is less intensively managed and could include orchards and ponds.

Zone Three on a large farm could include commercial crops combined with or preceded by a green manure cover crop to enrich the soil. Native trees or those needing minimal pruning would be situated here, as well as free-ranging herd animals.

Zone Four is an area for extensive tree culture and open pasture on larger farms. This area may border forest or wilderness, providing fuel and edible wild plants. Water can be stored here in dams, using wind energy to lift water to other areas.

Zone Five is "the natural, unmanaged environment used for occasional foraging, recreation, or just let be. *This is where we learn the rules that we try to apply elsewhere* [emphasis added]."[13]

The zones usually will not be perfectly concentric circles, as described above. For example, a rectangular property with the house set close to one end of the rectangle will have zones that move away from the house in slices. The idea is to think about the whole, no matter how large or small, and divide the whole into areas that correspond to use.

Part of the permacultural thinking about the whole also involves stepping back and looking at the big picture, the larger whole within which your own "little Eden" resides–that is, the unique bioregion or place on Earth you inhabit. This conforms to the idea in the new story of the universe of "knowing our place in the universe."

We are just beginning to immerse ourselves into learning about this bioregion and the Guadalupe River watershed of which we are a part. Sisterfarm is in a part of Texas that is said to be "at the edge of everything"–on the 30th latitude where equatorial storms stall, and the 100th longitude where the "dry line," running north to Canada, separates east from west. A practical result of this is that we have had to buy both eastern and western bird guides! Another result is that we are subject to weather extremes —droughts and floods.

In the first PowerPoint presentation we created about Sisterfarm, we summed up some aspects of our life in this particular bioregion as follows:

Learning to live with droughts, floods, hard pan, fire ants, Republicans, and other natural irritants.

Located in the south-central part of the Edwards Plateau—Sisterfarm is in a unique bioregion characterized by hills, rivers and creeks, and limestone outcroppings, known as "the Hill Country." The property is shaped like a triangle and is situated over the Trinity Aquifer, our sole source of drinking water. We are approximately forty-five miles northwest of San Antonio and live on the outskirts of the village of Welfare, which, as we tell our friends, is on the road to Comfort and not far from Utopia!

One hundred million years ago, this area formed part of the Bearpaw Sea, a shallow body of water that at one point extended from the Gulf of Mexico to the Artic, dividing the continent in two. The warm waters were habitat to rich aquatic life, the fossil remains of which we find here at Sisterfarm, most often in the form of white "heart stones" or fossilized clam shells. The fossil record shows that this area was inhabited by people as far back as 10,000 years.

PERMACULTURE IN PRACTICE I: A TOUR OF SISTERFARM

To illustrate how permaculture works in praxis, let me take you on a tour of Sisterfarm. Beginning with Zone Zero and moving out, I will describe our work from 1992 to the present. Although we didn't begin consciously to apply permacultural practices until ten years later, we more often than not instinctively acted in ways permacultural–with a few regrettable exceptions! Thus, I will describe what we have already done here, what we are now doing, and what we plan to do to embody permaculture values of "Earth care, people care, and fair share."

ZONE ZERO: THE HOUSE

The value of "people care" is lived out most extensively in Zone Zero–the house.

When we first saw this house in 1992, neither Elise nor I felt any attraction to it, but we loved the land, the creek, the native trees, and the birds. The house was too dark: brown paneling, heavy draperies, hanging cabinets that blocked light into the kitchen, and a porch overhang that blocked sunlight from coming into the dining room area.

I was much relieved when Elise spent the summer painting all of the paneling white. Both she and I grew up in sunny, warm places and we need lots of light to feel at home.[14] We were being attentive to our own *people care*.

My brother David came to visit us at Sisterfarm early on and gave generously of his time and talent. Since my father had been a plumbing and heating contractor, we both grew up around tools and machines and liked to hang out at his shops.

Dave and his wife, Sue, had already built two houses themselves, so he brought many skills to help us make Sisterfarm more inviting for all those who would live or visit here. He cut off the roof overhang outside the dining room, and "then there was light!" Next, he designed our first deck, which he built with our help and that of our friend Rafael Aldave.

The deck, which faces southeast toward the creek (located some 150 feet down a hill), is accessed from the dining room and has become the place for many gatherings, rituals, parties, and meetings. It's also great for dancing. Here is where Janie Barrera, one of our most faithful workers (and a founding board member of Santuario Sisterfarm), taught us to dance the two-step, Cotton-Eyed Joe, and a vigorous *Tejano* polka that always leaves us breathless. With the help of a dedicated group of "Friends of

Sisterfarm," like Janie, who have become our volunteer "working community," we later extended the deck so that the entire back of the house has decking.

One of the tenets of permaculture is to dissolve the boundaries between inside and outside living space. The decking does this, adding the equivalent of two more rooms for communal meeting space. With the heavy overhangs gone, the outdoor world is brought indoors.

Two other "people care" improvements involved renovating the kitchen, which we undertook in 1996

The Kitchen "Before"

when the cabinets began to collapse! The kitchen was too small to begin with, considering the many groups we had coming. My Adrian Dominican Hildegard Mission Group, for example, began meeting here once a year in the early 1990s and since we have a tradition of cooking together each time we gather, it was immediately evident that Sisterfarm's "one-butt" kitchen needed expanding.

My sister-in-law, Sue, was visiting at the time and she surprised us one day with sketches for a complete redesign of the kitchen, as well as for a ten-by-twelve-foot kitchen addition we eventually built and called the "Sprout Room." Besides her experience in actually building two houses, Sue was also a building inspector.

Sue's design included some open shelving on one end of the kitchen counter that now holds two-dozen glass canning jars with a variety of grains, including several types of rice, couscous, barley, and bulgur (wheat); a colorful assortment of beans; and edible seeds, such as flax, sesame, sunflower. Another set of shelves holds dried fruits, nuts, and pastas. As sunlight moves through and around the jars, the diversity of colors, shapes, textures, and sizes is intensified, as is my admiration and appreciation.

The Kitchen "After"

The Sprout Room actually lives up to its name. We grow sprouts here, and when we have groups of visitors or our cadre of volunteers from San Antonio, the extra sink and counters give us space for kitchen helpers to work in teams. Cooking together has been an important way for us to build relationships and connect with each other as we connect with the fruits of the Earth.

People care, of course, cannot really be separated from Earth care, since we are *of* Earth. One expression of Earth care in Zone Zero is our having converted to environmentally friendly household products and sending all kitchen "resources" (vegetable and fruit peelings, coffee grounds, egg shells) to the worm or compost bins, instead of treating them as garbage to be added to a landfill. Another is the newly installed graywater system, described in the section on Zone Two.

ZONE ONE: KITCHEN GARDENS, SHRINE, AND MEMORIAL GARDEN

Fortunately, even before we knew about permaculture concepts, we instinctively applied them in the placement of our gardens. We placed the herb garden right outside the Sprout Room and situated our vegetable garden where the previous owner had his —within the cyclone

Under construction:
The Gaia Garden
and Sprout Room (background)

fence that encloses the yard surrounding the house. It is on the way to the tool sheds, greenhouse, and compost bins.

The herb garden is in the shape of a circle, approximately fifteen feet in diameter, with four limestone paths leading to a central fountain and dividing the garden into four quadrants. It was designed by Elise's cousin, Jean Ponton, and friend Jeri Hesson, who named it the "Gaia Garden."[15]

The paths are laid out in the four directions, so

the garden gives us a constant sense of place, and the central three-tiered Mexican fountain, which was a gift from friends for my sixtieth birthday, has pro-

Gaia Garden with Sprout Room (on the left) and Cocky Shed (upper right)

vided habitat for frogs. Until we built this garden, we had hardly ever seen any frogs or toads here. As the lemon grass, lemon balm, sage, and salvias in the garden grew larger, and as we added more leaf mulch, the frogs have found safe places in which to hide when they jump out of the fountain.

Just beyond the Gaia Garden, our concrete water tank was turned into a tree-of-life mural by Elise's sister, Leslie. More recently, Leslie created a logo for Santuario Sisterfarm that also captures the spirit of our focus on cultivating diversity.

Zone One is home to our largest worm bin, which is in the carport next to the kitchen. After trying, without success, to grow worms in bins buried in the ground, we now have a successful vermi-composting operation that consists of three aboveground worm bins. The red wigglers consume our used office paper, which we shred, as well as coffee grinds and kitchen produce. The worms, in turn, provide us with a nutrient-rich soil enhancer in their castings (*i.e.*, worm manure).

The vegetable garden planted by the previous owner occupied a large patch in the sunny eastern corner of the yard. After our first year here, we converted

The first vegetable garden

the flat patch into seven rectangular raised beds and added a drip irrigation system. The paths in between were filled with cedar mulch that we shredded over a two-year period, during several of our famous Sisterfarm workdays. The previous owner had cleared a large amount of juniper cedar, which lay in decaying piles around the property. We have left a couple of these piles in place as habitat for birds, wild animals, and insects.

After seven years of rectangles, we felt drawn to refashioning the vegetable garden into a "Spiral Garden," a shape that reflects our feminist sensibilities, echoes the many spiral forms in nature, and provides a labyrinth-walking experience for all who enter it.

At the center of the Spiral Garden

The spiraling three-foot-wide bed with twenty-inch footpaths is divided into nine sections, each one named in honor of a Goddess or mythological woman from a different world culture, beginning with *Amaterasu*, the Japanese Sun Goddess of Agriculture and Weaving, and ending with *Yemanja*, the Yoruba Goddess of the Sea. In between, and among the others, is a bed named in honor of *Brigid*, the Celtic Goddess of Earth, Sea, and Sky, for all our Irish friends. Another, honoring *Dewi Sri*, the Rice Goddess of Bali, was suggested by Adrian Dominican Esther Kennedy, who spent a year in Indonesia studying Eastern culture and religious practices.

On the south side of Zone One, visible from the house, is a shrine to Our Lady of Guadalupe. The beautiful wooden *nicho* that holds the statue was a gift from María Berriozábal's father, Apolinár Rodríguez. It was the last thing he ever built. The clay statue of Guadalupe was a gift from our friend, Maureen Kelleher, for Elise at the time she became a Catholic. Our Lady of Guadalupe, *Lupita, La Virgen, Guadalupe-Tonantzin,* is revered by millions of people, especially, of course, Mexicans and Mexican Americans. My aunt Agnes, another convert, had such a great devotion to Our Lady of Guadalupe that she died holding her image—on December 12, 2001, Guadalupe's feast day!

During the January 2003 board meeting of Santuario Sisterfarm, María led us through a lovely ritual of rededication of the Guadalupe shrine, which we had moved into this zone so it would be closer to the house. Each of us participated in some special way. Since then we have planted several memorial bushes there, including a number of Texas natives.

María Antonietta Berriozábal
at the shrine to
Our Lady of Guadalupe

The "Berry Patch," running the twenty-foot length of the exterior wall of the living room, emerged this spring as a replacement for overgrown evergreen bushes. This bed earns its name by providing growing space for blueberries, strawberries,

53

and June berries. It also features a few hummingbird attractors, like the beautiful coral nymph salvia.

Just around the wall from the Berry Patch, tucked into a quiet corner is a meditation garden we created this year in memory of Ruth Remon McRae (1911-1996), thanks to a gift from her daughter, our Ursuline friend Kristen Wenzel. The "Garden of Ruth" features a small pond and waterfall inhabited by three goldfish and a number of frogs (last week I counted seven perched  on the lily pads, with a few others lurking behind rocks). Water lilies, papyrus, and other plants form part of the aquatic ecosystem, and the area surrounding the pond is planted with Texas native plants.

ZONE TWO: ORCHARD/GRAYWATER SYSTEM AND TOWER

For several years, we have wanted to create a graywater system at Sisterfarm that would enable us to recycle all the water we use in the house, except for toilet wastewater, for the purpose of irrigating plants and trees. In February 2003, we made the acquaintance of a young man from Austin, Kirby Frye, who had studied permaculture under Bill

Mollison and was available as a permaculture consultant.

With Kirby's help—and that of our longtime friend, Adrian Dominican Maureen Fenlon, who was spending three months with us[16]—we put in a graywater system and created a new orchard in a flat area just outside the fenced-in yard, in what we would consider to be Zone Two. It is a classic permacultural design, including "berms" and "swales" to create a natural rain-catchment system. The whole system enlivens the permaculture maxim that *the cheapest place to store water is in the soil.*

So now all the used house water, with the exception of toilet water, is funneled into one pipe that

The wick in process

carries the water underground, beyond the fence and into an eight-by-forty-foot area, known as a "wick," where it irrigates everything that is planted in it. That includes a mix of annuals and perennials, including nitrogen-fixing soybeans, along with blackberries, tomatoes, and eggplant. We dug the wick some eighteen inches deep, lined it with a thick rubber liner, and refilled the huge but shallow hole with about ten inches of gravel and four inches of rough native mulch, topping it off with soil. Now that the whole area is planted, visitors have no idea that this water-recycling system is in place.

Overflow from the wick flows underground through a pipe into a small, ten-foot diameter pond at the far right end of the wick. A slightly smaller, second pond, on the far left end of the wick is connected to the first pond by a "swale"–an old English word revived by permaculture to describe a gully-like ditch. If the first pond overflows, the water travels through the gravel at the base of the swale and into the second pond.

The soil we removed to create the two ponds and wick was used to build three long "berms," or mounds, about two feet high and four feet across, which run parallel to and the full length of the forty-foot-long wick.

We planted a wide variety of fruit and nut trees on the berms, including plum, apples, peaches, pine and hazel nuts, pecan, and pomegranate; sev-

Berms and swales in development

eral varieties of blueberries and strawberries; asparagus; and a number of annual vegetables, including

56

tomatoes, eggplants, lemon cucumbers, melons, and jicama. The swales run the full length of and in between each of the berms, and they are planted with alfalfa, crimson clover, and soybeans. Flat limestone rocks create a footpath in each of the swales and in designated places across the berms.

We have named this new orchard of berms and swales, ponds and wick, "Turtle Island"–the name Native American story gives Earth and North America.

Zone Two is also home to a tower we built in 1998 that has habitable rooms, where house guests often stay, in the two stories below the top deck.

The idea of a tower was inspired in August 1993 when our San Antonio friends and Sisterfarm workers Vangie Bazán X. and Susan Klein[17] came out to watch the night-sky Perseid meteor showers. We used a ladder to climb up onto our pitched roof where we lay on our backs to watch the annual nighttime spectacle of streaking meteor showers. That evening we sang a serenade of "oohs and ahs and wows and did you see that one?"–and hatched the idea of building *something* that would provide a more comfortable view of the meteor showers in the future, as well as a panoramic view of the surrounding Hill Country.

It took five years before we got to the tower project, but build it we did. Elise's brother, Danny, provided long-distance engineering assistance and

our San Antonio friend and builder, Jackie Currie, came out early to help us lay the foundation. Jackie and an all-women crew of *compañeras* (friends of the heart)–including Adrian Dominican physician Melba Beine; lawyers Yvonne Cherena Pacheco, Amy Kastely, and Mary Kenney; science teacher Robin Kessler; photographer Roberta Barnes; and visiting

friends Derre Ferdon of Tucson, Maureen Fenlon of California, Maureen Kelleher of Florida, and others – helped us build the tower over what turned out to be a year-and-a-half-long construction project.

The delay was due, in part, to a mishap that somewhat dampened our enthusiasm for working on the tower. I broke my hand working on the second-story railing. The break, a triple fracture of the metacarpal bone in my right (dominant) hand, kept me from manual labor for some time. But the good news is that it is now stronger than ever, with three screws holding the bone tightly in place!

We finished the tower the next spring and named her *"La Torre de Tonantzin,"* in honor of the Aztec Mother Earth Goddess. The ground floor Desert Room has a futon couch that converts into a full-size bed and a loft that can accommodate a second (limber) guest. The Meditation Room on the second floor has two large windows overlooking the ravine and enough space for a couple of inflatable mattresses.

The top deck of the tower is about twenty-three feet aboveground and it offers capacious views –at sunrise, sunset, and during starlit nights. It is a restorative place for cocktails after a day  of intense and sweaty labor, of which we have had many!

Almost every cleaning, clearing, or building project at Sisterfarm has been done with volunteer labor–from chipping and shredding a veritable mountain of juniper cedar to transplanting dozens of tomato plants. Our friends truly embody the permaculture ethic of *sharing time and labor for Earth care and people care*. But as they say of us: "Those

Proud tower builders

women at Sisterfarm work you hard, but they feed you incredibly healthy good meals, serve fine wine and beer, and throw great parties."

ZONES THREE AND FOUR: WALKWAYS AND WILD WAYS

In 1995, Elise and I planted an orchard closer to the entrance gate of Sisterfarm and thus, quite a bit farther away from the house than the Turtle Island orchard we put in during the winter 2003. It didn't work. The trees got diseased and never bore fruit.

One of the reasons why this orchard failed is that it was just too far away and out of sight. We didn't visit it on a daily basis or give it proper attention in a timely way. In permacultural terms, *it was placed in the wrong zone.* This bears out the old saying that the best fertilizer is the feet of the gardener. Or, as was said about Willy Loman in DEATH OF A SALESMAN, "Attention must be paid."

For now, the rest of Zones Three and Four at Sisterfarm are being left in their natural state with native trees, bushes, and wildflowers. The Big Joshua Creek runs through Zone Four, bordered by a 630-foot long and twelve-foot wide grassy area we call the "Meditation Walk."

Soon we will erect a "yurt"–a round portable structure designed by nomadic Mongolians–in a wooded area we call "Crone Grove," in Zone Three overlooking the creek. Accessible to the main house by walking along the "Maiden-Mother-Crone Path," the yurt will add meeting and sleeping space for visitors–expanding opportunities for others to experience the riches of this little corner of Earth.

"Three Sisters"–corn, beans, and squash
interplanted in the Spiral Garden

PERMACULTURE IN PRACTICE II:
LEARNING FROM NATURE

Bill Mollison says he coined the term "permaculture" because, in the early 1970s when he was thinking about these ideas, the concept of "sustainability" had not yet come into popular parlance. But creating sustainable ways of growing food is the underlying idea. Permaculture's basic practices are drawn from nature and imitate her ways.

For example, nature doesn't create a forest or a meadow in straight lines and out of a single species the way agribusiness grows most of our food crops. Nature loves a diversity of plants and animals and encourages useful connections between and among the plants and trees, the crawling creatures and the flying ones. There is, in short, a "useful connection" between the vine and the fig tree and us.

Nature's "polycultures" are self-organizing communities composed of many species. In a forest, for example, the trees are the *fixed* elements. They provide habitat for animals such as nesting materials, shelter, food, and places to hide and store food. In a mutually beneficial way, the animals and insects help the trees with pollination, seed dispersal, and pruning. Some trees act as a windbreak while others provide canopies for under-story trees and shrubs.

Trees create litter that forms an organic mulch layer around the trunk. Gradually, soil microorganisms decompose the mulch into humus, that earthy smelling, brown, porous, and spongy material that helps the soil function. One of our key tasks at Sisterfarm, where we have been buffeted by both long droughts and massive floods, is to work to increase the soil's capacity to hold moisture for later use. Again, *the best and cheapest place to store water is in the soil.*

Under the mulch layer, a wondrous community of microorganisms such as bacteria, fungi, and actinomycetes are quietly at work. Billions of these essential-to-life decomposers munch, crunch, encircle, suck on, break down and excrete the plant residue, fallen leaves, dead animals, and tree limbs. Other life forms, such as earthworms, continue the decomposing process, offering up the transformed nutrients and minerals that feed the soil, which in turn feeds the trees, shrubs, plants, animals—and us.

This web of life celebrates biodiversity and is sustainable, unlike the vast monocultures typical of modern agribusiness whose growth depends on huge doses of chemical fertilizers and pesticides that suppress the potential of microorganisms to do their work.

Permaculture creates sustainable ways to grow food by developing "edible ecosystems." The idea is to maximize yields by using all available space in a given area. We are urged to grow edibles horizontally, vertically, and as underground tubers; to maximize horizontal space by close intercropping; and to

use a fence, trellis, bamboo tipi, tall plant, or tree to support climbing fruits and vegetables.

The mainstays of an edible ecosystem are perennials, such as herbs, fruit and nut trees, tubers, and berries, interspersed with annuals. Among the edible perennial herbs we grow at Sisterfarm are *salad* herbs, such as sorrel, mint, pineapple sage, chives, salad burnet, lovage, fennel, and Mexican mint marigold. We also grow *tea*

The bean plants climb and twine around the corn.

herbs, including lemon grass, lemon balm, lemon verbena, borage, catnip, and the mints. And, of course, we grow *culinary* herbs, such as rosemary, thyme, tarragon, sage, oregano, cilantro, and peppermint.

Just listing these herbs makes me cheerful!

Additional fruit and nut trees we recently planted include paw paws, guava, mulberry, persimmon, jujube, Satsuma orange, Meyer's lemon, lime, and dwarf banana. We also are nursing two small avocado trees that we will transplant in the fall.

Among the tubers, we have planted horseradish, Jerusalem artichoke, potato, oca and yacon. These latter two, new to me, are native to South America and are used as we would potatoes. The berry plantings were described earlier.

Next year we plan to add kiwis and grapes along the orchard fences in Zone Two, and snap peas, climbing beans, cucumbers, and chayas along Zone One fences. The chaya, whose spinach-like leaves are incredibly nutritious, grows as a tree, and likes to be near a fence. Since this is a semi-tropical plant, the fence will make it easier for us to protect the chaya during a cold snap by draping a cover over it.

CREATE "GUILDS"

In permaculture, a "guild" is a human design for tree and plant placement that tries to learn from nature's polycultures. Bill Mollison describes a guild as a "harmonious assembly of species clustered around a central element (plant or animal). This assembly acts in relation to the element to assist its health, aid our work in management, or buffer adverse environmental effects."[18]

When I first began gardening behind the NET-WORK houses in Washington, D.C., I was a fanatical neat-nik. I used organic methods all right, but I wanted the rows of vegetables to be straight and tidy, the tomatoes to please stay inside their cages, the squash and melons to mind their manners and not spill over into the walkways. A group of Xaverian Brothers lived across from us and we could see each other's yards. They had a more casual approach to gardening–it appeared to me that they transplanted everything willy-nilly and simply flung the seeds out the kitchen door.

They thought I was a control freak.

Brother Tom More told me another brother had commented: "Carol stands on her back steps and yells, 'ATTENTION,' before she goes into her garden, and all the plants straighten right up and salute!"

Since then I have had a transformation of consciousness about "order" and "disorder," especially after studying permaculture principles, particularly the section on guilds in the book, GAIA'S GARDEN:

> ...[G]uilds ask for a subtle adjustment of our relations with our environment. The order of a conventional row-crop garden is the order of the machine. This regimentation invites us to view plants as mechanical

food factories. We fuel them with fertilizer, service them with rakes and hoes, and measure their production in bushels, bins, and tons. We view the plants as part of our dominion.

In a guild, we are but one living being among many others, and like all the other animals enfolded by this community, we nurture and are nurtured by an almost-wild place. ... We participate rather than rule. With guilds, we can begin to shed the mantle of command, and return to nature the many responsibilities we have unnecessarily assumed.[19]

As we planned Turtle Island, the Zone Two orchard created on top of the graywater wick and along the berms and swales, we tried to keep the elements of a guild in mind and to look for as many useful connections as possible. In permaculture, all plants, trees, shrubs, and herbs should be planted with their multi-functions in mind.

Before we planted anything, we added an organic soil food and soft rock phosphate to the whole area. Next we broadcast red clover, alfalfa, and soybean seeds.

Red clover is a soil-improvement plant and, as a legume, it can take nitrogen from the air and store it in root nodules, until it is passed on to the soil. It also has an extensive root system that can bring up trace minerals deep in the soil, as well as provide food for the earthworms, who, in turn help aerate the soil. Its leaves decay rapidly and make great compost. Their red flowers add a welcome bit of color and are loved by the bees.

Alfalfa, another legume, is valuable as a perennial green manure cover crop: it provides vegetative cover to help prevent erosion and can be cut and tilled in place or just left on top of the soil to provide organic matter. In addition, its root system is extensive, able to penetrate the soil twenty or more feet. These roots help break up clay soil and, as they decay, provide nutrients deep in the soil for the use of other plants. Like clover, alfalfa is a valuable nitrogen fixer, plus its purple flowers add another touch of color.

We planted lots of soybeans because they also fix nitrogen and help with erosion. Soybeans have high protein content and in Japanese restaurants the steamed and salted green beans, or *Edamame*, are served as a delicious and nutritious appetizer.

These three crops are now growing throughout the berms, along with perennials such as asparagus, globe artichoke, comfrey, and Jerusalem artichoke. The undulating asparagus ferns offer visual delight, help stabilize the edge of the berm, and will reappear annually as an early spring crop. The globe artichoke provides food, a point of vertical and horizontal interest, and when cut back, its large leaves become mulch. Comfrey, considered an over-achiever in multi-functionality, holds soil, produces mulch, is consumed by animals, and is able to pull potassium and other minerals into its leaves. It also can be made into a tea for human consumption or to fertilize other plants.[20]

One of my favorite multi-function plants is the Jerusalem artichoke, perhaps because I first made her acquaintance in my Washington gardens. She was so easy to grow—a real no-brainer. And once you introduce a Jerusalem artichoke into your garden, it is literally "until death do us part." They will appear and reappear wherever slivers of the tuber are left in the ground. If a sliver lands in the compost bin, watch out! Ecstatic growth ensues.

A stand of Jerusalem artichokes can be a wind-break, a dramatic border on one edge of the garden, or a hedge or divider. The edible tubers that grow underground look like small potatoes. They can be sliced into salads, chilled in lemon water and sprinkled with salt. They can be roasted, steamed, boiled, or sautéed. Their carbohydrates, in the form of inulin instead of starch, are particularly useful in a diabetic's diet. The tubers also can be fed to pigs. (We're going to see if our three dogs are interested.)

In the Spiral Garden this year we grew a guild of three plants that Native Americans refer to as the

"Three Sisters"–corns, beans, and squash. Nearby, we planted an insectary plant, *Gregg's Mistflower*, a Texas native perennial, which strengthened the guild's interactions because the bees and butterflies that are attracted to it help pollinate. The beans fix the nitrogen used by the corn and squash. The corn provides a place for the beans to climb up and around, and the squash takes up the ground level. After harvesting, all the plant remains will be added to the compost pile.

Conserve Water

None of the practices I have just described could be implemented if we did not have a plentiful supply of water. All life depends on it, and a permacultural ethic demands that we do everything possible to protect and conserve water.

Indian physicist and ecologist Vandana Shiva writes: "In 1995, Ismail Serageldin, vice president of the World Bank, made a much-quoted prediction about the future of war: 'If the wars of this century were fought over oil, the wars of the next century will be fought over water.'"[21]

Shiva refers to the water crisis as the "most pervasive, most severe, and most invisible dimension of the ecological devastation of the Earth."[22] Finding ways to conserve water–in the soil and elsewhere–are fundamental aspects of permaculture design. In drought-prone south Texas, conserving water is an imperative.

Three years ago, we purchased five ninety-gallon rain barrels made of recycled plastic and originally designed by employees of the City of Vancouver in British Columbia, Canada. This enlightened city government subsidized the purchase of these barrels to encourage its citizens to save water.[23] It only takes an inch or so of rain to fill them up. It's amazing to think of how much water we could save around the globe by capturing the rainwater off our roofs instead of letting it go down the drain—and it's somewhat disconcerting to think of how much is being lost without these simple old-fashioned aids.

To further conserve water, we recently invested in a new drip irrigation system, which was installed in the major growing areas at Sisterfarm. The drip hose is a few inches under the topsoil so the water goes directly into the root areas at twelve-inch intervals. This conserves more water than an above-ground sprinkler system, where much of the water evaporates.

In the near future, we hope to install a more capacious rain-catchment system that will be connected to the drip irrigation so that nearly all of our crop-watering needs can be handled by recycled water.

BEYOND MANICURED LAWNS

My heart is moved by all I cannot save:
so much has been destroyed
I have to cast my lot with those
who age after age, perversely,
with no extraordinary power,
reconstitute the world.[24]

This fragment of a poem by Adrienne Rich comforted me many a time during my NETWORK days, as we kept plodding away, trying to shift national public policy from benefiting only the privileged few and toward the common good of all people

Now, as my sense of the common good has expanded to embrace all of creation, my heart indeed does grieve for all I see that has been destroyed–and for all that will be destroyed if we don't change our ways. However, I take heart when I remember that NETWORK began with a small group of women religious, an even smaller budget, and with our having minimal knowledge of the legislative process. In its thirty-year history, membership expanded from the original forty-seven to more than 12,000 activists nationally, and NETWORK has become a respected and sustained voice for justice in Washington.

Without the initial and continued support of women religious who cast their lot with us financially, we could not have succeeded. So I wonder now what religious congregations could do to help reverse the pillaging of Earth, the abuse of her water, air, and land.

One very visible action, a metaphor of the transformation we must undergo, might be for us to overthrow the tyranny of the manicured lawn! Our ubiquitous and perfectly ordered lawns are symbolic of our disordered relationship with Earth. The care and upkeep of trophy lawns is an example of our mindless misuse of nature's gifts.

And here I must confess: I used to think tidy lawns were great. Growing up in Florida, I had been acculturated to think that manicured lawns–full of the same kind of grass, uniformly green, and with perfectly straight edges–were an admirable goal for any homeowner.

I have since learned that lawns as we now know them were developed by the English upper class. Being wealthy enough not to have to utilize all your land for food growing was a status symbol. So having a large grassy area with neat rows of flowers placed in formal patterns in front of your mansion called everyone's attention to your social standing in the community.

In the United States, our addiction to the tyranny of neatly cut lawns can be traced back to golf courses. As golfing grew more popular (I also confess to playing golf a few times), players began to seek the same kind of "greens" for their own lawns.

Water-guzzling, chemical-using, and labor-demanding lawns have become a national preoccupation, almost an obsession. Unfortunately, the motherhouses, Catholic schools, universities, and healthcare facilities of religious congregations all seem captive to this same addiction.

I suggest that we consider transforming our manicured lawns because it would be such a visible and teachable sign of the much larger shift in consciousness about Earth and sustainability that we humans must undergo if life is to survive.

What would happen if we women religious, healthcare administrators, or parish staff intentionally returned all our motherhouse, hospital, or church lawns to natural prairies of indigenous grasses and wild flowers? What if we created an edible landscape of perennial fruits, nuts, and berries that modeled ways of growing healthy food locally?

How radical would it be if we started planting vines and fig trees?[25]

Carol and Janie Barrera design the shape of the
pond in the Garden of Ruth.

Carol and Tamayo enjoy the completed
Garden of Ruth.

FINDING YOUR OWN VINE
AND FIG TREE

Writing this "little book" has taken me on a journey through my life. It has been like walking the Chartres-style labyrinth at our motherhouse, first going in one direction, then in another, back and forth, with life's turns, passing by paths taken earlier,

 but always moving deeper toward the center. Here, I pause and gather memories embedded in the turns.

I remember my early experiences of the victory garden, the failed garden, and my first organic garden and see their influences in stirring in me a deep yearning for a place under a (real) vine and fig tree.

And just during the past month, three new experiences have rekindled in me a keen awareness of the animating impulses I mentioned at the start of this book: a search for the Divine and meaningful ritual, a love of the outdoors, an appreciation of diversity, and a commitment to social justice.

I conclude by sharing these experiences.

The first was a weeklong retreat sponsored by the Congregation of Divine Providence in San Antonio on the words of Jesus in the "Our Father" and the "Beatitudes," based on translations of the original Aramaic by Neil Douglas-Klotz.[26] We learned the Aramaic pronunciation of the prayers, reflected on the multi-layered meanings of the words, and then learned chants and body movements for each line. At the end of the week we put it all together, and for an hour and forty minutes, we chanted and danced the prayer, beginning with *Abwoon d'bwashmaya* ("O Birther! Father-Mother of the Cosmos").

I loved every minute of it and felt I could have gone on chanting and dancing much longer. It was such a contemplative and integrated–body, mind, spirit–way to pray. And hearing the Beatitudes translated as, "Blessed are those who plant peace each season," connected me in a new way with our permaculture goals at Sisterfarm.

The second experience took place a week later. Nancy Sylvester invited me to attend a conference with her in Goshen, New York, on "Happiness, Freedom and Justice: A Feminist Perspective," organized by Blauvelt Dominican Arlene Flaherty. Ivone

Gebara, a Brazilian Sister of Our Lady and an eco-feminist theologian, was the presenter and Janet Walton, S.H.N.J. coordinated the prayer and rituals, several of which were done outdoors.

During the five-day conference, Ivone led us through an examination of the three words–happiness, freedom, and justice–at a personal and societal level. The conference planners invited a diverse group of women to participate, understanding that cultural background, ethnicity, age, politics, and religious experience impact our worldviews.

The women, ranging in age from the mid-twenties into the seventies, came from Afghanistan, Brazil, Chile, Democratic Republic of the Congo, the Dominican Republic, Pakistan, Peru, the United States, and Uruguay. We talked about how our personal stories and worldviews affect our understandings and experiences of happiness, freedom, and justice.

A vivid memory I have of this gathering is hearing firsthand about the destruction, torture, pain, and despair occurring in Afghanistan, Pakistan, Brazil, and the Congo–and feeling profound sorrow, anger, and frustration about the injustices being perpetrated, many by our government, in our name, all over the globe. Despite the pain–or perhaps *through* it–we were able to dance and play musical instruments together.

A Pakistani woman demonstrated a dance from her country and we all tried to imitate her hand motions. An Uruguayan woman taught us the *paso doble*; an Afghani woman drummed the beat used to accompany women dancing with veils; and I taught two dances, using music by Jewish cantors and a Romanian folksong. We also learned a Brazilian

Carol thanks Nasreen Daniel for teaching Pakistani dances.

samba and Dominican Republic merengue.

Being together for those days was like forming a guild in a permaculture garden. Each of us brought her own experiences to the daily discussions and her gifts of music, dance, poetry, or story telling to the evening gatherings. The whole-of-us together was so much richer than our separate parts.

The third experience–the burial of Thaddeus "Spike" Zywicki (1911-2003)–took place on July 18, 2003, at the Sisters of the Holy Spirit Motherhouse in San Antonio. Spike had $400 to his name when he died at the age of ninety-one, so the sisters offered to have him buried in their cemetery. Several of Spike's friends dug the grave by hand to save money and another friend e-mailed information about Spike's last days and death, along with a request for donations to help cover the other funeral costs. It was so like Spike to pull off this group effort!

I have known Spike since 1973 when he was in his early sixties. A diminutive man whose full white beard added to his elfish appearance, Spike loved NETWORK and became one its strongest members and supporters.

When Spike lived in San Antonio, he often got on the tourist bus that circled around the city all day. He'd strike up a conversation with people (in his demonstration voice, which carried throughout the bus) and ask about their representatives in Congress, whipping out the NETWORK voting record to let the hapless tourists know if their elected leaders voted "right" or not!

Spike embodied permaculture's Earth-care, people-care, and fair-share values, although he had already set his life course long before these concepts were articulated.

His early life experiences of polio, separation from his parents, and growing up in an orphanage made him sensitive to the poor and marginated of the world. He lived five years in a Catholic Worker House near the U.S. Capitol, and then ten years in Mexico fighting the exploitation of the Mexicans by transnational corporations, many of them U.S.-owned. Spike wrote: "These experiences convinced me that my job was to come back and let the people of my country know what we were doing to the

Mexican people. My work then began to follow these lines: leafleting in the Washington area, attending Congressional hearings, sending occasional newsletters, and participating in the Human Rights movement."

It was at this point, in 1973, that Spike and I connected. And during his burial service in 2003, I realized that *Spike was responsible for my being at Sisterfarm.*

Spike had met Barbara Aldave in 1982 on the east steps of the U.S. Capitol where Barbara was standing with a group of others participating in a NETWORK prayer and vigil demonstration. When Spike learned that Barbara taught law, he told her about the lawsuit he had brought against Chief Justice Warren Burger, challenging a law that forbade the distribution of political literature on the grounds of the Supreme Court building. Barbara recalls saying something to the effect of "Uh-huh, sure."

But immediately after Barbara returned to her home in Austin, Texas, the newspapers began to run stories about the difficulty the Supreme Court was facing in deciding whether to decide a case nominally brought against its Chief. An appeal was granted in 1982 under the name *United States v. Grace* (the name of the other co-plaintiff) and in 1983, in what many consider a landmark decision, the high court ruled in favor of the plaintiffs.

At the end of the 1980s, when Barbara was serving as president of the board of NETWORK (and still teaching law in Texas), she received notice that she had been nominated to apply for the deanship at St. Mary's University School of Law in San Antonio. In the course of events when, months later, she was about to be publicly introduced as the new dean of the law school at St. Mary's, Barbara asked the university president, "By the way, who nominated me?" The president pulled out the nominating letter and before he uttered a word, Barbara knew who it was when she saw the holes in the stationery where there should have been "o's," recognizing it was a product of Spike's ancient typewriter!

Around that same time, Elise had begun working with NETWORK in a consulting capacity, helping to renew the organization's publications and strengthen its fundraising and membership development. Impressed with Elise's work, Barbara invited her to apply for position in communications and fundraising at the law school.

The rest, as they say, is history. Elise got the job. I was ready to leave Washington after twenty years. Nancy Sylvester was stepping down as the second director of NETWORK and going on sabbatical. So all three of us moved to Texas in 1992 and, finally, I was able to begin to live my long-held dream—settling down on a piece of land and planting real vines and fig trees.

The only catch is, I don't get to sit under them often enough!

But the riches of living my dream in the sacred Earth of Sisterfarm and being able to practice permaculture values, impels me to encourage others to find their own ways of engaging in "Earth care, people care, and fair share."

So much has been destroyed, yet –

Elise just told me she saw tiny figs on one of the newly planted trees ....

NOTES

[1] 1 Maccabees 14:11, with inclusive language.

[2] For a fuller account, see Carol Coston, O.P., "Women Religious Engage the Political Process," JOURNEYS IN FAITH AND FIDELITY, ed. by Nadine Foley, O.P. (New York: Continuum, 1999), pp. 198-217.

[3] For a fuller account, see Carol Coston, O.P., "Women Religious Invest in Their Values," JOURNEYS IN FAITH AND FIDELITY, ed. by Nadine Foley, O.P. (New York: Continuum, 1999), pp. 218-241.

[4] A mission group is the smallest unit in the government structure of the Adrian Dominican Sisters.

[5] Bill Mollison, PERMACULTURE: A PRACTICAL GUIDE FOR A SUSTAINABLE FUTURE (Washington, D.C.: Island Press, 1990), p. ix.

[6] Red Tomato, a non-profit worker-owned organization on whose board I serve, is a pioneering example of groups committed to strengthening small family farmers and sustainable agriculture by expanding local markets for their products (see www.redtomato.org).

[7] Mollison, PERMACULTURE, p. ix.

[8] Bill Mollison, with Reny Mia Slay, INTRODUCTION TO PERMACULTURE (Australia: Tagari Publications, 1991), p. v.

[9] In a 1991 video, "Global Gardener: Permaculture with Bill Mollison," Mollison shows creative examples of sustainable agricultural practices in the tropics, arid lands, cool climates, and urban environments. (Bullfrog Films, P.O. Box 149, Oley, PA 19547; 800/543-3764; www.bullfrogfilms.com)

[10] Mollison and Slay, INTRODUCTION TO PERMACULTURE, p. 3.

[11] *Ibid*.

[12] Ursula Goodenough, THE SACRED DEPTHS OF NATURE (New York: Oxford University Press, 1998), p. 87.

[13] Mollison, PERMACULTURE, p. 50.

[14] Elise's father was a U.S. diplomat, so the family moved around quite a bit. Her early childhood was spent in Mexico and Uruguay, and she later lived in Egypt and Guatemala.

[15] Gaia—a Greek Earth Goddess—refers to the "Gaia Theory," developed by scientist James Lovelock. The theory holds that Earth is living entity, a super self-regulating organism.

[16] Maureen Fenlon spent three months at Sisterfarm as part of a yearlong exploration of ecological centers and initiatives created by women religious. She

recently accepted a position as interim director of NETWORK!

[17] Susan and Vangie have recently combined their design and computer skills to form the San Antonio design firm of Sister Creek Studios (www.sistercreekstudios.com), which is responsible for designing the "Dominican Women on Earth" series and will soon create a website for Santuario Sisterfarm.

[18] Mollison, PERMACULTURE, p. 60.

[19] Toby Hemenway, GAIA'S GARDEN: A GUIDE TO HOME-SCALE PERMACULTURE (White River Junction, Vermont: Chelsea Green Publishing Company, 2001) p. 166.

[20] Madalene Hill and Gwen Barclay with Jean Hardy, SOUTHERN HERB GROWING (Fredricksburg, Texas: Shearer Publishing, 1987), p. 80.

[21] Vandana Shiva, WATER WARS: PRIVATIZATION, POLLUTION, AND PROFIT (Cambridge: South End Press, 2002), p. ix.

[22] *Ibid.*, p. 1.

[23] See www.rainpail.com for more information.

[24] Rich, Adrienne, "Natural Resources," THE DREAM OF A COMMON LANGUAGE (New York: W.W. Norton & Company, Inc., 1978), p. 67.

[25] Several congregations already have taken significant steps toward thinking and acting sustainably. Please see the "Note" on p. 103 for examples.

[26] Neil Douglas-Klotz, PRAYERS OF THE COSMOS: MEDITATIONS ON THE ARAMAIC WORDS OF JESUS (HarperSanFrancisco: 1990).

RECOMMENDED RESOURCES

Below is a list of books that were influential in Carol Coston's thinking about ecology and permaculture and inspire her current work at Santuario Sisterfarm.

Appelhof, Mary. WORMS EAT MY GARBAGE. Illustrated by Mary Frances Fenton. Kalamazoo, Michigan: Flower Press, 1982.

Beck, C. Malcolm and J. Howard Garrett. TEXAS ORGANIC VEGETABLE GARDENING. Houston: Lone Star Books, 1999.

Creasy, Rosalind. THE COMPLETE BOOK OF EDIBLE LANDSCAPING. Illustrated by Marcia Kier-Hawthorne. San Francisco: Sierra Club Books, 1982.

Gebara, Ivone. LONGING FOR RUNNING WATER: ECOFEMINISM AND LIBERATION. Trans. David Molineaux. Minneapolis: Fortress Press, 1999.

Goodenough, Ursula. THE SACRED DEPTHS OF NATURE. New York: Oxford University Press, 1998.

Hemenway, Toby. GAIA'S GARDEN: A GUIDE TO HOME-SCALE PERMACULTURE. White River Junction, Vermont: Chelsea Green Publishing Company, 2001.

Hill, Madalene and Gwen Barclay with Jean Hardy. SOUTHERN HERB GROWING. Fredericksburg, Texas: Shearer Publishing, 1987.

Jeavons, John. HOW TO GROW MORE VEGETABLES (THAN YOU EVER THOUGHT POSSIBLE ON LESS LAND THAN YOU CAN IMAGINE). Berkeley: Ten Speed Press, 1979.

Kingsolver, Barbara. SMALL WONDER. New York: Harper Collins Publishers, 2002.

Mollison, Bill with Reny Mia Slay. INTRODUCTION TO PERMACULTURE. Tyalgum, Australia: Tagari Publications, 1991.

POSTSCRIPT: ABOUT THIS SERIES

Beginning in the thirteenth century, a new form of theology emerged in which women, "for the first time in Christianity, took on an important, perhaps even preponderant role," writes Bernard McGinn in the introduction to MEISTER ECKHART AND THE BEGUINE MYSTICS.[1]

"Vernacular" theology differed both in content and audience from the academic concerns of scholastic theology and the biblical commentary of monastic theology. Written not in Latin but in the spoken language of medieval people, vernacular theology "implied a different and wider audience than that addressed by traditional monastic and scholastic theology."[2]

Among those who contributed significantly to the body of vernacular theology were the Beguines, women in Europe who took up a nontraditional form of independent and apostolic religious life beginning in the twelfth century.

Written by nontraditional women in a nontraditional language, the vernacular teachings also came in nontraditional forms.

According to McGinn, "Much of it was expressed in sermonic form, though of many kinds. A wide variety of treatises and 'little books' were employed, as well as hagiography and letters. Poetry was also of significance."[3]

We draw upon this rich thirteenth-century tradition in publishing this series of "little books," written by Dominican women in a vernacular created out of the soil of their experience of living into new ways of being human, at the dawn of the twenty-first century. These new ways of being are impelled by an inchoate awareness of our place in the universe and by the shocking awareness of an imperiled Earth.

The first awareness: In the last quarter of the twentieth century, insights gleaned from new scientific understandings about the nature and origin of our universe have been applied by a host of writers in a variety of fields, including theology, to revisit assumptions derived from a more than 300-year-old understanding of the universe as a static, mechanistic, and hierarchically ordered object. The writings reflect the profound psychic shift we have undergone in seeing, for the first time in human history, our home planet from outer space; in learning about the deep interconnectedness of all life; in reawakening, through scientific inquiry, to the ancient revelation of "Oneness" that all our spiritual traditions teach; and in understanding our place in the universe as a self-aware, conscious species inhabiting a "privileged" planet, where life has emerged through an epic fourteen-billion-year journey that is still unfolding in form and consciousness.

The second: With the public stir created by the publication of Rachel Carson's SILENT SPRING in 1962, as Springfield Dominican Sharon Zayac points out in EARTH SPIRITUALITY: IN THE CATHOLIC AND DOMINICAN TRADITIONS[4], the modern environmental movement began. Since then, innumerable reports, studies, and books have been written, documenting the extraordinary assault on Earth's life systems undertaken by humans during the past 100 years. Life on Earth has not been this threatened since sixty-five million years ago when, as scientists now believe, a six-mile-wide asteroid plunged into the ocean off the Yucatan Peninsula. Dinosaurs were among the many species that went extinct in the ensuing nuclear darkness; it took some ten to fifteen million years for Earth to recover from the disaster.[5]

In response to these signs of the times, many groups and individuals around the globe have begun to act, including women religious. Among congregations of Catholic Sisters, many are approaching their own "motherlands" differently: conserving land, creating wildlife habitat, letting fields lie fallow, converting to organic growing, exploring alternative energy usage. A number of women religious around the world have established ecological centers dedicated to teaching Earth literacy, modeling ways of living lightly on the land, understanding systemic connections of oppression among all forms of domination, exploring Earth spirituality, cultivating diversity, and nurturing sustainable relationships among all creation.

Of the three-dozen or so ecological centers and initiatives that have been created by women religious in the United States, more than one third were founded or co-founded by Dominican sisters (see list on p. 98). Best known among these is Genesis Farm, founded in 1980 by Caldwell Dominican Miriam Therese MacGillis, whose inspiring example helped give birth to so many of the other centers.

The authors of this series are Dominican women who, like Miriam and women in other religious communities, are living into and sharing new ways of being human on Earth. Actually, these are ways that indigenous peoples have long known and lived and that all humans are now being called to learn, drawing on their own spiritual traditions, if our species is to survive.

For many Catholics, the unfolding "Universe Story" and "new" Earth spirituality are wonder-filled invitations to go deeper into the mysteries of their faith; to plumb its incarnational and sacramental essence. Teilhard de Chardin grasped the awesomeness of it all when he wrote:

> The sacramental Species are formed by the totality of the world, and the duration of the creation is the time needed for its consecration.[6]

Seven hundred years earlier, Beguine mystic Mechtild of Magdeburg (1210-c1280) had intuited this Oneness, writing:

> The day of my spiritual awakening
> was the day I saw
> and knew I saw
> all things in God
> and God
> in all things.[7]

More practical than mystical, Sor Juana Inés de la Cruz (1648-1695) – the Mexican nun, scientist, poet, musician, and scholar whose memory is honored by the Sor Juana Press – dedicated herself to "reading" the natural world through observation on the several occasions when she was forbidden to read books. Believing that knowledge of the arts and sciences was the path to knowledge of God, Sor Juana wrote:

> It seem[s] to me debilitating for a Catholic not to know everything in this life of the Divine Mysteries that can be learned through natural means....[8]

It is our hope that these "little books" will stimulate an engaging *conversatio* ("living with a familiarity that includes but is not limited to verbal discussion"9) among women religious and others about both the issues each author presents and the spiritual journey she shares. In particular, we hope that each "little book" will stimulate deep *conversatio* around questions of faith, spirituality, and Divine consciousness.

- Editors

[1]MEISTER ECKHART AND THE BEGUINE MYSTICS, ed. by Bernard McGinn (New York: Continuum, 1994), p. 6.
[2]*Ibid.*, p. 8.
[3]*Ibid.*, p. 9.
[4]Sharon Zayac, O.P., EARTH SPIRITUALITY: IN THE CATHOLIC AND DOMINICAN TRADITIONS, "Dominican Women on Earth," ed. by Elise D. García and Carol Coston, O.P. (San Antonio, Texas: Sor Juana Press, 2003), p. 18.
[5]See Tim Flannery, THE ETERNAL FRONTIER: AN ECOLOGICAL HISTORY OF NORTH AMERICA AND ITS PEOPLES (New York: Grove Press, 2001), pp. 9-24.
[6]Pierre Teilhard de Chardin, THE DIVINE MILIEU (New York: Harper & Row, Publishers, 1968), p. 126.
[7]Sue Woodruff, MEDITATIONS WITH MECHTILD OF MAGDEBURG (Santa Fe, New Mexico: Bear & Company, Inc., 1982), p. 42.
[8]Sor Juana Inés de la Cruz, "Response to the Most Illustrious Poetess Sor Filotea de la Cruz," A WOMAN OF GENIUS: THE INTELLECTUAL AUTOBIOGRAPHY OF SOR JUANA INÉS DE LA CRUZ, trans. by Margaret Sayers Peden (Lime Rock Press, Inc.: Salisbury, Connecticut, 1982), p. 32.

[9]See McGuinn, MEISTER ECKHART, p. 8, where he refers to "Meister Eckhart's 'conversation' with the Beguines (understood in the Latin sense of *conversatio*, that is, living with a familiarity that includes but is not limited to verbal discussion)" as providing "a particularly instructive example" of ways in which "medieval mystical texts challenge stereotypes about men and women..."

ECOLOGY/ECOSPIRITUALITY CENTERS

Established by Women Religious in the United States

(Known to editors as of August 2003)

ALLIUM
LaGrange Park, Illinois
Sisters of St. Joseph of LaGrange

THE BRIDGE BETWEEN
Denmark, Wisconsin
Sinsinawa Dominican Sisters

CEDAR HILL ENRICHMENT CENTER
Gainsville, Georgia
Adrian Dominican Sisters

CENTER FOR EARTH SPIRITUALITY AND RURAL MINISTRY
Mankato, Minnesota
School Sisters of Notre Dame

CHURCHES' CENTER FOR LAND AND PEOPLE
Sinsinawa, Wisconsin
Sinsinawa Dominican Sisters

CLARE'S WELL
Annandale, Minnesota
Franciscan Sisters of Little Falls

CROWN POINT ECOLOGY LEARNING CENTER
Bath, Ohio
Sisters of St. Dominic of Akron

CRYSTAL SPRING
Plainville, Massachusetts
Kentucky Dominican Sisters

DOMINICAN REFLECTION CENTER
Edmonds, Washington
Dominican Sisters of Edmonds

EARTHEART
La Casa de María Retreat Center
Santa Barbara, California
La Casa de María/Immaculate Heart Community
Sisters of St. Joseph, Los Angeles Province
Religious of Sacred Heart of Mary, Western America
Province

EARTHLINKS
Denver, Colorado
Loretto Community
Dominican Sisters of Hope

EVERGREEN
Villa Maria, Pennsylvania
Sisters of Humility of Mary at Villa Maria

FRANCISCAN EARTH LITERACY CENTER
Tiffin, Ohio
Tiffin Franciscans

FRANKLIN FARM
Manchester, New Hampshire
Sisters of Holy Cross

FULL CIRCLE ECOHOUSE OF PRAYER
Port Huron, Michigan
Sisters of Mary Reparatrix

GENESIS FARM
Blairstown, New Jersey
Caldwell Dominican Sisters

GRAILVILLE
Loveland, Ohio
Grailville Community

GREEN MOUNTAIN MONASTERY
North Chittenden, Vermont
Passionist Sisters of the Earth Community

HEARTLAND FARM AND SPIRITUALITY CENTER
Pawnee Rock, Kansas
Great Bend Dominican Sisters

JUBILEE FARM
New Berlin, Illinois
Springfield Dominican Sisters

MERCY ECOLOGY INSTITUTE
Madison, Connecticut
Sisters of Mercy

MICHAELA FARM
Oldenburg, Indiana
Sisters of St. Francis of Oldenburg

NAZARETH FARM AND CENTER FOR
ENVIRONMENTAL SPIRITUALITY
Kalamazoo, Michigan
Sisters of St. Joseph of Nazareth

PRAIRIE WOODS FRANCISCAN SPIRITUALITY CENTER
Hiawatha, Iowa
Franciscan Sisters of Perpetual Adoration

RED HILL FARM
Acton, Pennsylvania
Sisters of St. Francis of Philadelphia

SANTUARIO SISTERFARM
Welfare, Texas
Adrian Dominican Sisters

SHEPHERD'S CORNER
Blacklick, Ohio
Columbus Dominican Sisters

SIENA SPIRITUALITY CENTER
Water Mill, New York
Amityville Dominican Sisters

SISTERS HILL FARM
Bronx, New York
Sisters of Charity New York

SOPHIA GARDEN AND LEARNING CENTER
Amityville, New York
Amityville Dominican Sisters

SPRINGBANK RETREAT CENTER
Kingstree, South Carolina
Adrian Dominican Sisters
Sisters of St. Francis of Oldenburg

ST. CATHARINE FARM/DOMINICAN EARTH CENTER
St. Catharine, Kentucky
Dominicans of St. Catharine

WATERSPIRIT
Elberon, New Jersey
Sisters of St. Joseph of Peace

WHITE VIOLET CENTER FOR ECO-JUSTICE
Saint Mary-of-the-Woods, Indiana
Sisters of Providence of Saint Mary-of-the-Woods

THE WOODLANDS
Osseo, Wisconsin
Sisters of St. Francis of Assisi

Note: In addition to establishing ecology and/or ecospirituality centers, women religious in the United States and in a number of countries around the world are engaged in an array of activities aimed at conserving land, promoting sustainable practices, restoring natural habitats, and modeling new ways of living lightly on Earth. Descriptions of a number of these efforts can be found on the website of the National Catholic Rural Life Conference (see www.ncrlc.com) and in the annotated directory of members of Sisters of Earth, a network of women dedicated to healing Earth's community of life, founded in 1994 by a group of concerned women religious (see www.sistersofearth.org). As more centers are identified, we will include them in next publication.

Among the many outstanding examples of ecological efforts underway is the "Ecovillage" project completed in April 2003 by the Sisters, Servants of the Immaculate Heart of Mary (IHMs) of Monroe, Michigan. The IHMs invested $56 million in a massive effort to renovate their 376,000-square-foot motherhouse in an environmentally conscious way, developing, among other things, geothermal wells for heating and cooling and a graywater system for reusing water that will cut consumption by thirty-five percent (see www.ihmsisters.org).

Several communities have established congregation-wide ecology committees, such as the Loretto Community's Earth Network Coordinating Committee, to share information, plan ecology projects, sponsor educational events, and motivate the membership to a deeper ecological sensitivity. Some congregations focus on raising ecological consciousness and practices at their motherhouses. For example, the Adrian Dominicans' Earth Stewardship Committee sponsors educational seminars. It also has set up an ecology resource room, coordinated the establishment of a wetlands and a Cosmic Walk on campus grounds, and advocated successfully the switch to chlorine-free post-consumer recycled paper for office supplies.

Others are involved in inter-congregational efforts. In 1998, twelve congregations of women religious, along with other Catholic institutions that own land in the Hudson River bioregion of New York, set up ROAR (Religious Organizations Along the River) to "support one another in using our lands with an attitude of respect for beauty and integrity of Earth" and to "address the interrelated issues of poverty, justice and ecology in this bioregion."